Success
Learn and Practise

Maths
age 9-10 · level three

YEAR
5

Paul Broadbent

Contents

Using and applying mathematics

Counting and understanding numbers

Knowing and using number facts

Calculating

Understanding shape

Measuring

Handling data

Glossary

Answers

Word problems

Answering problems

If you have a word problem to solve, try using these four stages.

A bag costs £6.80. What change would there be from a ten-pound note?

1 Read the problem. Try to picture the problem and imagine going through it in real life.
2 Sort out the calculations. Find the **difference** by counting on from £6.80 to £10.
3 Answer the calculations. £10.00 – £6.80 is £3.20.
4 Answer the problem. Look back at the question – what is it asking?

The change from a ten-pound note for the bag is £3.20.

Multi-step problems

Word problems can have different numbers of calculations to answer before you reach the final answer.

One-step problems
There are 185 boys and 217 girls in a school. What is the **total** number of children?

185 + 217 = 402   402 children in total.

Two-step problems
900g of flour and 500g of sugar are mixed together and then divided equally into two bowls. What is the weight of the mixture in each bowl?

Step 1
900g + 500g = 1400g

Step 2
1400 ÷ 2 = 700g

So there is 700g of mixture in each bowl.

Key words   difference   total

4

Answering problems

1 There are 270g of cake mixture in a bowl. It is divided equally between 9 bun cases. What is the weight of the mixture in each case?

☐ g

2 Robert is one-fifth of his mother's age. If his mother is 35, how old is Robert?

☐

3 From Leeds, it is 81km to Manchester and 62km to York. How much further is it from Leeds to Manchester than to York?

☐ km

4 A hall has 265 chairs in total. At a concert all but 25 chairs are used. How many people are at the concert?

☐

5 A bike costs £136 and a helmet costs £35. How much do they cost altogether?

£ ☐

6 A regular hexagon has 6 equal sides. Each side is 9cm in length. What is the distance around the whole hexagon?

☐ cm

6

Multi-step problems

1 There are 4 weeks and 5 days until Rebecca's birthday. How many days is it in total until her birthday? _____

2 Sam picks 58 apples and Ryan picks 62 apples. They put them together and then divide them equally between 6 bags. How many apples are in each bag? _____

3 Claire has 43 sweets to put into 9 party bags for her friends. How many will there be in each bag and how many will be left over? _____

4 Mr Benson posts 3 parcels. Two of the parcels cost £3.20 each and the other parcel costs £2.35. What is the total cost of posting the three parcels? _____

4

TOTAL MARKS 10

5

Problem-solving

Reasoning

If you need to think carefully about a way to solve a problem, you are likely to be using reasoning skills to make sense of it. It may help to explain the problem to someone else, describing the way you could try to solve it.

What colour is each shape?

Clues:
- there are three colours used
- yellow is not next to green
- the red square is next to the circle

- the green square is between two red shapes
- the squares are not yellow.

To answer questions like this, draw the shapes and find the clues that give the most help. The third clue shows that the first square is red. That means that the second square is green and the triangle is red. The circle must be yellow.

Always check each clue with your answer to make sure it is correct.

Finding all possibilities

These types of problems often have lots of different choices of answer and the skill is finding the correct one. You need to work systematically, making lists of all the possible answers to find the right one.

Find three **consecutive** numbers that add up to 39.

1 Trial and improvement method:

$14 + 15 + 16 = 45$.

It must be less:

$12 + 13 + 14 = 39$.

2 Using reasoning:

$39 \div 3 = 13$.

This must be the middle number:

$12 + 13 + 14 = 39$.

Key words   consecutive

Reasoning

1 Tom is 9 years old. His father is 36 years old. How many years older is Tom's father? Circle which of these you could use to work this out.

27

36 + 9   45 – 9   45 – 34   36 – 9   36 × 9   36 ÷ 9

2 I am thinking of a number. If I double it, the answer is 34. If I subtract 6 from it, the answer is 11. What number am I thinking of?

17

3 Zoe has some sweets in a box. She takes 5 out and then divides the rest equally into two bags. There are 14 sweets in each bag. How many sweets did she have in the box?

3?

4 Use the clues to work out the colour of each shape.

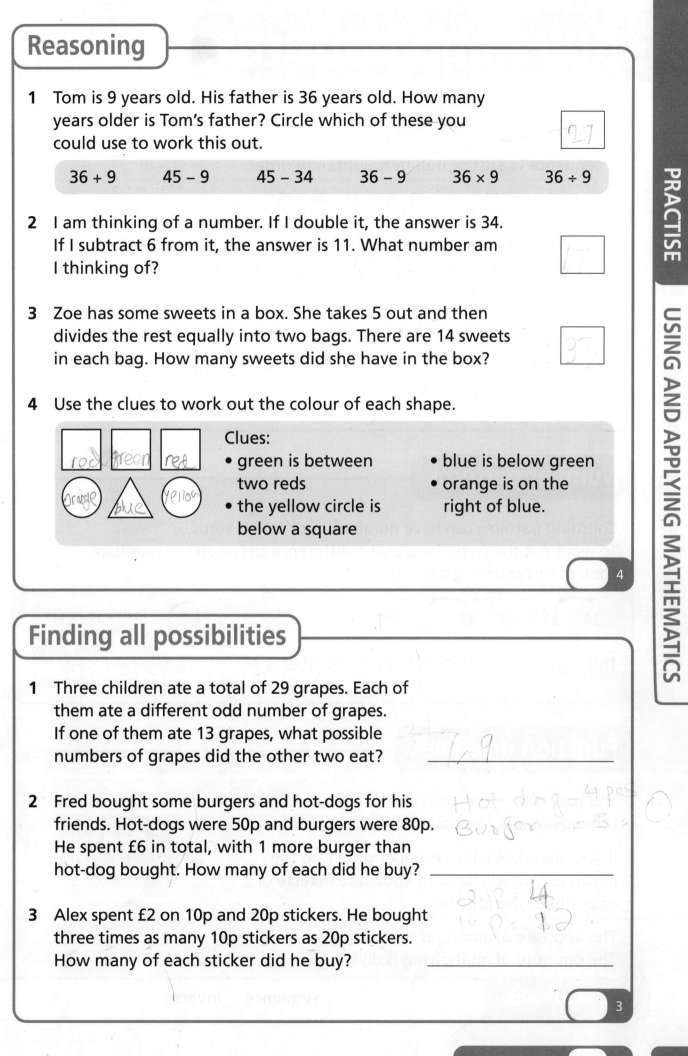

red   green   red
orange   blue   yellow

Clues:
- green is between two reds
- the yellow circle is below a square
- blue is below green
- orange is on the right of blue.

4

Finding all possibilities

1 Three children ate a total of 29 grapes. Each of them ate a different odd number of grapes. If one of them ate 13 grapes, what possible numbers of grapes did the other two eat? _____ *7, 9*

2 Fred bought some burgers and hot-dogs for his friends. Hot-dogs were 50p and burgers were 80p. He spent £6 in total, with 1 more burger than hot-dog bought. How many of each did he buy? _____ *Hot dog = 4 pcs Burger = 5*

3 Alex spent £2 on 10p and 20p stickers. He bought three times as many 10p stickers as 20p stickers. How many of each sticker did he buy? _____ *20p = 4 10p = 12*

3

Rules and patterns

Number sequences

A **sequence** is a list of numbers written in order.

> 7 8 9 10 11   43 42 41 40 39

If you need to find missing numbers in a sequence, look carefully at the numbers you are given. Try to work out the numbers next to these first, then write the others.

> 127 128 ____ ____ 131 ____

So in this sequence, 129 follows 128, then the next number is 130.
Which number follows 131?

Number patterns

Counting patterns can have numbers in different steps.
To work out the steps, look at the difference between the numbers.
Look at this counting pattern.

> 34   37   40   43   ____

This is going up in threes. The next number is 46.

Top Tip
To help you work out the missing number, draw 'jumps' between each number and write the differences.

Function machines

You may have questions which ask you to find the numbers going in and coming out of a function machine.

If you are asked which number goes into the machine, you will need to know the **inverse** or opposite of the function.

$6 \rightarrow$ IN ×4 OUT $\rightarrow 24$

The opposite of adding is subtracting.
The opposite of multiplying is dividing.

Key words   sequence   inverse

Number sequences

Write the missing numbers in each sequence.

1   47   48   [49]   [50]   51   52   [53]

2   163   [164]   165   [166]   167   [   ]   169

3   [81]   [80]   79   78   [   ]   76   75

4   297   298   299   [   ]   [   ]   [302]   303

5   402   401   [400]   [   ]   398   397   [   ]

5

Number patterns

Continue these sequences in both directions.

1   [39]   [45]   51   57   63   [69]   [75]

2   [   ]   [   ]   32   39   46   [   ]   [   ]

3   [   ]   [   ]   40   36   32   [   ]   [   ]

4   [   ]   [   ]   81   86   91   [   ]   [   ]

4

Function machines

Write the numbers coming out of these function machines.

1   49   →   IN   ÷7   OUT   →   [7]

2   32   →   IN   +25   OUT   →   [   ]

Write the numbers going into these function machines.

3   [   ]   →   IN   −9   OUT   →   24

4   [7]   →   IN   ×8   OUT   →   56

4

Place value and decimals

4-digit numbers

Look at these numbers and how they are made.

The position of a **digit** in a number is really important. 1572 and 7125 use the same digits, but they are very different numbers. Always check where you put each digit when you write numbers.

Decimal numbers

Decimal numbers are whole numbers divided into tenths and hundredths. A decimal point is used to separate whole numbers from decimals. Look at these number lines.

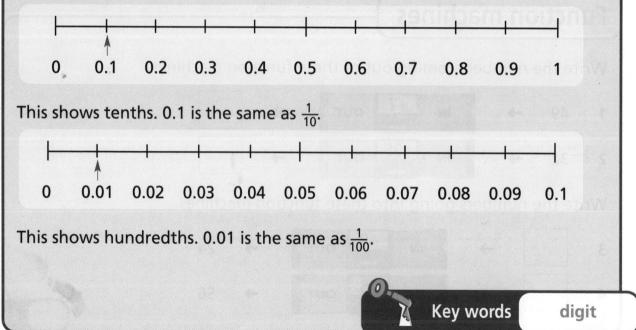

This shows tenths. 0.1 is the same as $\frac{1}{10}$.

This shows hundredths. 0.01 is the same as $\frac{1}{100}$.

Key words   digit

10

4-digit numbers

Write these number words as numerals.

1   nine thousand six hundred and forty-two   9642

2   four hundred and twenty-five   425

3   three thousand two hundred and thirteen   3213

4   one thousand five hundred and ninety-eight   1598

5   six thousand and seventy   6070

6   two thousand and fifty-eight   2058

7   eight thousand three hundred and sixty   8360

8   seven thousand and nine   7009

8

Decimal numbers

Write the missing numbers in the boxes on these number lines.

1 7.1   2 7.5   3 8.2   4 8.8

5 3.4   6 3.7   7 4.3   8 4.9

8

Comparing numbers

Comparing numbers

< and > are really useful symbols ... but don't get them confused!

< means 'is less than'   45 < 59   45 is less than 59.

> means 'is greater than'   142 > 124   142 is greater than 124.

When you need to compare two numbers, you must look carefully at the value of the digits.

Which is bigger, 87 or 78?

87 is the same as 80 + 7,

78 is the same as 70 + 8,

So 87 is bigger than 78.

Ordering numbers

If you have a list of numbers to put in order, it is a good idea to put the numbers into groups with the same number of digits.

For each group, arrange them in order of size, depending on the place value of the digits.

1 Put these in order, starting with the smallest.

600   3110   305   3200   529   1008   2945

2 Group the hundreds, then the thousands and put them in order.

600   305   529   →   305   529   600

3110   3200   1008   2945   →   1008   2945   3110   3200

3 Put them all together in order.

305   529   600   1008   2945   3110   3200

Comparing numbers

Write the correct < or > sign in each box.

1   56   ☐<   93

2   87   ☐>   78

3   44   ☐>   42

4   19   ☐   61

5   53   ☐   35

6   220   ☐<   310

7   964   ☐>   938

8   572   ☐<   575

9   414   ☐>   141

10   883   ☐>   838

10

Ordering numbers

Write each set of numbers in order of size, starting with the smallest.

smallest .... largest

1   385   198   296   258 | 198 | 258 | 296 | 385 |

2   597   527   592   572 | 527 | 572 | 592 | 597 |

3   1043   4130   3014   4301 | 1043 | 3014 | 4130 | 4301 |

4   2665   2556   2656   2566 | 2556 | 2566 | 2665 | 2656 |

5   712   294   367   248 | 248 | 294 | 367 | 712 |

6   399   3939   393   9339 | 393 | 399 | 3939 | 9339 |

6

Estimating

Rounding

Rounding a number to the nearest ten is useful for **estimating**.
A 'round number' is a number ending in zero, such as 10, 20, 30, 40, 50, 60, 70, 80, 90 or 100.

Rounding is easy if you follow these two simple rules.

To round to the nearest 10, look at the 'ones' digit. Then ...
1   If it is 5 or more, round up the tens digit.
2   If it is less than 5, the tens digit stays the same.

So 84 rounds down to 80.

137 rounds up to 140.

265 rounds up to 270.

Half-way numbers ending in 5, such as 165, 145 and 385, always round up to the next ten.

137 140

Top Tip *Remember, a number is always between two possible 'round' numbers – you just have to choose which one it is nearest to.*

Approximate answers

Estimating is a bit like guessing – but we use information for an **approximate answer**, rather than a wild guess!

Always work out an approximate answer before you calculate, then you will know if your actual answer makes sense. Use rounding skills to work out an approximate answer for the following example.

There are 38 magazines in a box. How many are there in 9 boxes?

38 rounds up to 40.

$40 \times 9 = 360$

38×9 is approximately 360.

Key words   rounding   estimating   approximate answer

Rounding

Round each of these numbers to the nearest 10.

1 64 ➡ 60

2 72 ➡ 70

3 38 ➡ 40

4 55 ➡ 60

5 911 ➡ 910

6 426 ➡ 430

7 803 ➡ 800

8 145 ➡ 150

8

Approximate answers

Circle the number that is nearest to the correct answer for each of these.

1 47 + 32 = 70 80 90

2 19 + 27 = 50 40 30

3 82 + 71 = 140 150 160

4 91 – 18 = 80 70 60

5 66 – 41 = 20 30 40

6 102 – 39 = 80 70 60

7 23 × 7 = 210 200 140

8 38 × 4 = 120 160 180

8

TOTAL MARKS 16

Fractions

Types of fractions

Look at these three types of fraction.

A **proper fraction**, such as $\frac{3}{5}$, which is less than 1.

An **improper fraction**, such as $\frac{9}{4}$, which is greater than 1.

$$\frac{9}{4} = 2\frac{1}{4}$$

A **mixed number**, such as $2\frac{1}{4}$, which has whole numbers and fractions.

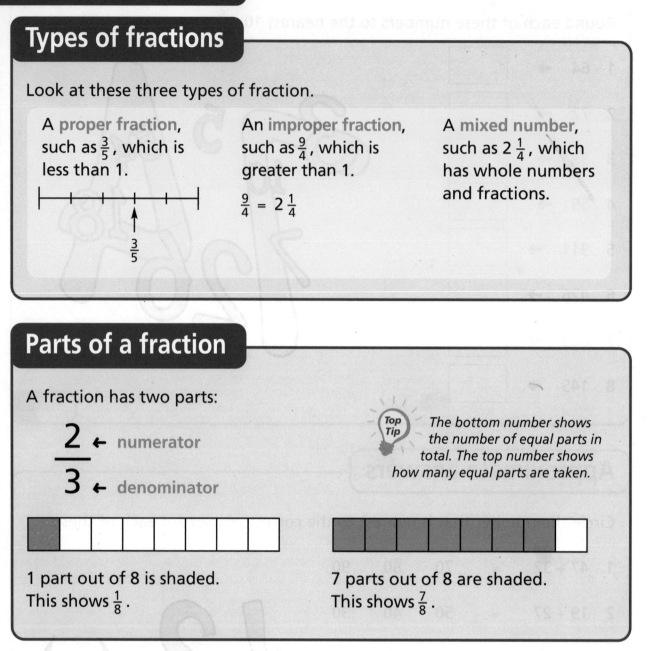

$$\frac{3}{5}$$

Parts of a fraction

A fraction has two parts:

$$\frac{2}{3}$$

2 ← numerator

3 ← denominator

Top Tip *The bottom number shows the number of equal parts in total. The top number shows how many equal parts are taken.*

1 part out of 8 is shaded. This shows $\frac{1}{8}$.

7 parts out of 8 are shaded. This shows $\frac{7}{8}$.

Equivalent fractions

Equivalent fractions are worth the same, even though they may look different. Imagine cutting a pizza into quarters and eating two of the pieces. Eating $\frac{2}{4}$ of a pizza is the same as eating $\frac{1}{2}$ of the pizza.

Key words   proper fraction   improper fraction   mixed number
numerator   denominator   equivalent fractions

Types of fractions

Put a tick (✔) in each column to complete this table.
One has been done for you.

	$\frac{7}{3}$	$4\frac{2}{5}$	$\frac{10}{9}$	$\frac{4}{5}$	$\frac{3}{7}$	$3\frac{2}{3}$	$\frac{5}{2}$
Proper fraction							
Improper fraction	✔						
Mixed number							

6

Parts of a fraction

Write the fraction of each shape shaded blue.

1

2

3

4

5

6

6

Equivalent fractions

Circle two fractions with the same value in each set.

1 $\frac{4}{6}$ $\frac{2}{10}$ $\frac{1}{2}$ $\frac{1}{4}$ $\frac{3}{6}$

2 $\frac{1}{4}$ $\frac{1}{2}$ $\frac{4}{10}$ $\frac{2}{8}$ $\frac{1}{5}$

3 $\frac{2}{6}$ $\frac{1}{4}$ $\frac{1}{2}$ $\frac{1}{3}$ $\frac{1}{5}$

4 $\frac{2}{5}$ $\frac{2}{20}$ $\frac{2}{10}$ $\frac{1}{12}$ $\frac{1}{10}$

5 $\frac{1}{3}$ $\frac{3}{9}$ $\frac{3}{10}$ $\frac{2}{3}$ $\frac{2}{9}$

5

Addition and subtraction facts

Number facts

You need to know all of your number bonds to 20.
Number bonds are the addition and subtraction facts within 20.

Here are some examples.

7 + 7	7 + 8	7 + 9
16 – 6	16 – 5	16 – 4

You can use these facts to add and subtract tens.

3 + 5 = 8	9 – 6 = 3
3 tens + 5 tens = 8 tens	9 tens – 6 tens = 3 tens
30 + 50 = 80	90 – 60 = 30

Top Tip *If you start at 0 and count on in tens, you will find multiples of 10.*
10 20 30 40 50 60 70 80 90 100

Trios

The three numbers 8, 5 and 3 are called a trio.
They can make four addition and subtraction facts.

3 + 5 = 8   5 + 3 = 8   8 – 5 = 3   8 – 3 = 5

If you learn your addition facts, you can use them to help with subtraction.

4 + 9 = 13   ☐ – 9 = 4   13 – ☐ = 9

Top Tip *Remember that 4 + 6 gives the same answer as 6 + 4. It doesn't matter which way round you add. Once you know one fact, you know the other.*

Key words   multiple

Number facts

Answer these additions and subtractions.

1 2 + 9 = [ ]

2 12 − 4 = [ ]

3 8 + 7 = [ ]

4 16 − 3 = [ ]

5 11 + 6 = [ ]

6 70 − 50 = [ ]

7 30 + 40 = [60]

8 90 − 80 = [10]

9 60 + 20 = [ ]

10 100 − 50 = [ ]

10

Trios

Use these trios to find the missing numbers in each addition and subtraction.

| 4 | 5 | 9 |

| 3 | 10 | 7 |

| 8 | 6 | 14 |

1 4 + 5 = [9]

4 [ ] − 7 = 3

2 9 − [ ] = 5

5 14 − 8 = [6]

3 7 + 3 = [10]

6 8 + [ ] = 14

6

TOTAL MARKS [16]

Multiplication facts

Times tables

Learning your tables will make the rest of the maths easier. Once you know these, you will never forget them.

On the grid, try to find $6 \times 4 = 24$.

You will see it is written twice, showing that the answer is the same for both: $6 \times 4 = 4 \times 6$.

×	1	2	3	4	5	6	7	8	9	10
1	1	2	3	4	5	6	7	8	9	10
2	2	4	6	8	10	12	14	16	18	20
3	3	6	9	12	15	18	21	24	27	30
4	4	8	12	16	20	24	28	32	36	40
5	5	10	15	20	25	30	35	40	45	50
6	6	12	18	24	30	36	42	48	54	60
10	10	20	30	40	50	60	70	80	90	100

Write down any facts you are not sure of and try to learn them. Use other facts to help.

8×3 is **double** 4×3.

9×3 is 3 less than 10×3, which is 27.

7×4 is double 7×2. Double 14 is 28.

Once you learn these, you can try your 7, 8 and 9 times tables.

Top Tip These are the facts for the tables that probably cause the most problems:

6 x 3	7 x 3	8 x 3	9 x 3
6 x 4	7 x 4	8 x 4	9 x 4

Learn one fact a day – it will only take 8 days!

Multiples

It is useful to be able to recognise multiples of 2, 5 and 10.

Multiples of 2 end in **0, 2, 4, 6, 8**.

18 is a multiple of 2.

Multiples of 5 end in **0 or 5**.

35 is a multiple of 5.

Multiples of 10 end in **0**.

60 is a multiple of 2, 5 and 10.

Key words   double   even number

Times tables

Answer these questions.

1 $7 \times 2 = $ ☐

2 $5 \times 4 = $ ☐

3 $3 \times 6 = $ ☐

4 $4 \times 4 = $ ☐

5 $9 \times 5 = $ ☐

6 What is three multiplied by nine? ☐

7 Multiply seven by four. ☐

8 Double eight. ☐

9 There are six cakes in a packet. How many cakes are there in five packets? ☐

10 There are seven days in a week. How many days are there in ten weeks? ☐

Top Tip *Remember that even numbers are all multiples of 2.*

10

Multiples

Use this list of multiples to answer each question.

| 50 | 15 | 8 | 14 | 9 | 20 |

1 Which numbers are multiples of 10? _____

2 Which numbers are multiples of 2? _____

3 Which numbers are multiples of 5? _____

4 Which number is a multiple of 5, but not a multiple of 2 or 10? _____

5 Which two numbers are multiples of 2, but not multiples of 10 or 5? _____

6 Which two numbers are multiples of 3? _____

6

TOTAL MARKS ☐ 16

Division facts

KNOWING AND USING NUMBER FACTS

LEARN

Dividing

Dividing is the opposite of multiplying. It is the same as sharing or grouping.

These both show 15 divided by 3.

15 sweets shared between 3.
There are 5 in each group.

$15 \div 3 = 5$

15 sweets grouped into 3s.
There are 5 groups.

$15 \div 3 = 5$

Top Tip Remember that multiplication and division are *inverses* (opposites). Because of this, division can be checked by multiplying.
$35 \div 5 = $ ➔ $5 \times 7 = 35$ ➔ so $35 \div 5 = 7$

Missing number problems

15, 5 and 3 are a special set of numbers. We call them a trio, as you will have read on page 18.

$3 \times 5 = 15$ $5 \times 3 = 15$ $15 \div 3 = 5$ $15 \div 5 = 3$

Knowing your trios can help work out missing number problems.
2, 6 and 12 are another trio. Use them to find the missing numbers.

$2 \times \underline{\quad} = 12$ $\underline{\quad} \times 2 = 12$ $12 \div \underline{\quad} = 6$ $\underline{\quad} \div 6 = 2$

Key words   inverse

Dividing

1 Divide twelve by three. `4`

2 How many fives are there in forty? `8`

3 What is twenty-eight shared equally between four? `7`

4 What is half of eighteen? `9`

5 A class of 32 children are put into 4 equal teams. How many children are in each team? `9`

6 How many 5p stamps can be bought with 30p? `6`

7 27 counters are divided equally between 3 pots. How many counters will there be in each pot? `9`

8 There are 28g of yoghurt in a pot. Half the yoghurt has been eaten. How much yoghurt is left? `12` g

8

Missing number problems

Write the missing numbers.

1 70 ÷ `7` = 10

2 `8` × 2 = 16

3 4 × `5` = 20

4 45 ÷ `9` = 5

5 `6` × 3 = 18

6 `14` ÷ 2 = 7

7 5 × `5` = 25

8 24 ÷ `6` = 4

1.) 5 × 5 = 25
2.) 25 ÷ 5 = 5
3.) 10 ÷ 2 = 5
4.) 3 × 5 = 15
5.) 45 ÷ 9 = 5

8

TOTAL MARKS 16

Mental addition and subtraction

Adding 2-digit numbers

If you need to add two big numbers, it helps to
break the numbers up and add the tens,
then add the ones.

15 + 37 = ____

Use these three steps.

1 Hold the bigger number in your head: 37.

2 Break 15 into 10 + 5. Then add the tens: 37 + 10 = 47.

3 Finally, add the ones: 47 + 5 = 52.

Counting on

A really good method for a take-away or subtraction is to find the
difference between the numbers by counting on.

What is the difference between 18 and 34?

18   20   34

This number line shows exactly what goes on in your head.

Count on from 18 to 20. Hold the 2 in your head.

20 to 34 is 14.   14 + 2 is 16.   So 34 − 18 = 16.

2

Top Tip *If it helps, draw a quick number
line and show the steps. Remember
to put the smallest number on the
left and the largest on the right.*

Adding 2-digit numbers

Calculate these additions and write the matching letters to find the code words. Each letter is worth one mark.

1 14 + 23 = [ ] ➜ [C]

   64 + 11 = [ ] ➜ [A]

   34 + 24 = [ ] ➜ [T]

2 28 + 35 = [ ] ➜ [D]

   59 + 22 = [ ] ➜ [ ]

   33 + 16 = [ ] ➜ [ ]

3 24 + 25 = [ ] ➜ [G]

   37 + 44 = [ ] ➜ [ ]

   48 + 27 = [ ] ➜ [ ]

   19 + 39 = [ ] ➜ [T]

4 23 + 35 = [ ] ➜ [ ]

   45 + 36 = [ ] ➜ [ ]

   56 + 19 = [ ] ➜ [ ]

   17 + 46 = [ ] ➜ [ ]

14

Counting on

Read and answer these questions.

1 What is the difference between 29 and 52?

2 How much less is 38 than 83?

3 Calculate the difference between 47 and 15.

4 How much more is 64 than 43?

5 Find the difference between 16 and 39.

6 What is the difference between 21 and 78?

6

TOTAL MARKS [ ] 20

Written addition

Written method for adding

If you are given a sum and the numbers are too big or there are too many numbers to add in your head, then you need to use a written method.

417 + 265 Follow this step-by-step method.

1   Write them in a **column**, lining up the units digits.

```
    417
+   265
```

2   Start by adding from the right-hand column, the units column. Any total over 9, just put the tens digit under the next column.

```
    417
+   265
    682
    1
```

3   Now do the same with the tens column. Keep going left until all the columns have been added.

```
    417
+   265
    682
    1
```

> **Top Tip** Work out an approximate answer first. 417 + 265 is approximately 400 + 300, which is 700. You can then check if your answer is close to your *estimate*.

Adding money

It can be a bit confusing if you need to add mixed amounts of pounds and pence. What is the total cost of a drink that is £1.60 and a cake at 79p?

Try changing the pence to pounds, lining up the decimal point.

```
    1.60
+   0.79
    2.39
    1
```

£1.60   79p

The total cost is £2.39.

🔑 **Key words**   column   estimate

Written method for adding

Calculate these additions.

1　　408
　　+ 257

2　　361
　　+ 429

3　　515
　　+ 185

4　　146
　　+ 277

5　Add together 362 and 539.

6　What is the total of 444 and 198?

7　Calculate 207 + 595.

8　Add 487 and 416.

```
  515
+ 185
```

8

Adding money

Calculate the total cost.

£3.40　　£1.09　　£1.59　　75p　　88p

1　　　　£ ▢

2　　　　£ ▢

3　　　　£ ▢

4　　　　£ ▢

5　　　　£ ▢

6　　　　£ ▢

7　　　　£ ▢

8　　　　£ ▢

8

TOTAL MARKS　16

27

Written subtraction

Column method

If you cannot work out a subtraction in your head, this is one method you can try.

What is 874 subtract 138?

Step 1	Step 2	Step 3
Rename $70 + 4$ as $60 + 14$.	$60 - 30 = 30$	$800 - 100 = 700$
$14 - 8 = 6$		

$$
\begin{array}{r}
8\,^6\!7\,^1\!4 \\
-\ 1\,3\,8 \\
\hline
6
\end{array}
\qquad
\begin{array}{r}
8\,^6\!7\,^1\!4 \\
-\ 1\,3\,8 \\
\hline
3\,6
\end{array}
\qquad
\begin{array}{r}
8\,^6\!7\,^1\!4 \\
-\ 1\,3\,8 \\
\hline
7\,3\,6
\end{array}
$$

Top Tip

Important! Remember to always take the bottom number away from the top number.

Number line method

Another written method is to use a number line to find the difference between the numbers by counting on.

What is 173 subtract 138?

1 Draw a blank number line from 138 to 173.

2 Count on to 140, then to 173 to find the difference.

3 Add up all the jumps.

$2 + 33 = 35$, so the difference between 138 and 173 is 35.

Column method

Complete these subtractions.

1
```
    4 9 3
  -  1 5 5
  _____
```

4
```
    8 2 6
  -  2 1 8
  _____
```

2
```
    7 0 2
  -  6 8 2
  _____
```

3
```
    5 3 7
  -  1 4 9
  _____
```

5 Subtract 165 from 368.

6 What number is 294 less than 750?

7 Calculate 411 – 172.

8 What is 603 minus 359?

9 What is 527 subtract 188?

9

Number line method

Use the number lines to answer these.

1 What is the difference between 436 and 481?

436   481

2 What is the difference between 597 and 617?

597   617

3 What is the difference between 215 and 400?

215   400

4 What is the difference between 350 and 523?

350   523

4

TOTAL MARKS   13

Multiplication

Mental calculations

If you know your tables, then multiplying numbers to 20 by a single digit can be worked out in your head.

What is 13 multiplied by 4?

Use these three steps.

1 Multiply the tens: $10 \times 4 = 40$.

2 Multiply the units: $3 \times 4 = 12$.

3 Add the two parts: $40 + 12 = 52$.

Top Tip
To multiply tens by a single digit, work out the fact and then make it ten times bigger:

$60 \times 4 = 6 \times 4 \times 10 = 24 \times 10 = 240$

Written methods

To work out a multiplication such as 38×5, you need to be able to multiply multiples of 10.

$38 = 30 + 8$

$+$

$38 \times 5 \quad \rightarrow \quad 30 \times 5 = 150$

$\qquad\qquad\qquad\qquad 8 \times 5 \;\; = \;\; \underline{40} \; +$

$\qquad\qquad\qquad\quad 38 \times 5 \;\; = \;\; 190$

Look at these two methods for this.

$$\begin{array}{r} 3\,8 \\ \times \quad 5 \\ \hline 190 \\ \hline 4 \end{array}$$

x	30	8
5	150	40

$150 + 40 = 190$

Answers

PAGE 5

Answering problems

1	30g	4	240
2	7 years old	5	£171
3	19km	6	54cm

Multi-step problems
1 33
2 20
3 4 sweets in a bag and 7 left over
4 £8.75

PAGE 7

Reasoning
1 27 years older
   36 – 9
2 17
3 33
4

Red   Green   Red

Yellow   Blue   Orange

Finding all possibilities
1 1 and 15, 3 and 13, 5 and 11, 7 and 9
2 4 hot-dogs and 5 burgers
3 4 20p stickers and 12 10p stickers

PAGE 9

Number sequences
1 47, 48, **49**, **50**, 51, 52, **53**
2 163, **164**, 165, **166**, 167, **168**, 169
3 **81**, **80**, 79, 78, **77**, 76, 75
4 297, 298, 299, **300**, **301**, **302**, 303
5 402, 401, **400**, **399**, 398, 397, **396**

Number patterns
1 **39**, **45**, 51, 57, 63, **69**, **75**
2 **18**, **25**, 32, 39, 46, **53**, **60**
3 **48**, **44**, 40, 36, 32, **28**, **24**
4 **71**, **76**, 81, 86, 91, **96**, **101**

Function machines

1	7	3	33
2	57	4	7

PAGE 11

4-digit numbers

1	9642	5	6070
2	425	6	2058
3	3213	7	8360
4	1598	8	7009

Decimal numbers

1	7.1	5	3.4
2	7.5	6	3.7
3	8.2	7	4.3
4	8.8	8	4.9

PAGE 13

Comparing numbers

1	56 < 93	6	220 < 310
2	87 > 78	7	964 > 938
3	44 > 42	8	572 < 575
4	19 < 61	9	414 > 141
5	53 > 35	10	883 > 838

Ordering numbers
1 198, 258, 296, 385
2 527, 572, 592, 597
3 1043, 3014, 4130, 4301
4 2556, 2566, 2656, 2665
5 248, 294, 367, 712
6 393, 399, 3939, 9339

PAGE 15

Rounding

1	60	5	910
2	70	6	430
3	40	7	800
4	60	8	150

Approximate answers

1	80	5	30
2	50	6	60
3	150	7	140
4	70	8	160

PAGE 17

Types of fractions

	$\frac{7}{3}$	$4\frac{2}{5}$	$\frac{10}{9}$	$\frac{4}{5}$	$\frac{3}{7}$	$3\frac{2}{3}$	$\frac{5}{2}$
Proper fraction				✔	✔		
Improper fraction	✔		✔				✔
Mixed number		✔				✔	

Parts of a fraction

1	$\frac{1}{5}$	4	$\frac{4}{7}$
2	$\frac{1}{12}$	5	$\frac{3}{10}$
3	$\frac{5}{6}$	6	$\frac{7}{9}$

Equivalent fractions

1	$\frac{1}{2}$ and $\frac{3}{6}$	4	$\frac{2}{20}$ and $\frac{1}{10}$
2	$\frac{1}{4}$ and $\frac{2}{8}$	5	$\frac{1}{3}$ and $\frac{3}{9}$
3	$\frac{2}{6}$ and $\frac{1}{3}$		

PAGE 19
Number facts
1	11	6	20
2	8	7	70
3	15	8	10
4	13	9	80
5	17	10	50

Trios
1	9	4	10
2	4	5	6
3	10	6	6

PAGE 21
Times tables
1	14	6	27
2	20	7	28
3	18	8	16
4	16	9	30
5	45	10	70

Multiples
1	50 and 20	4	15
2	50, 8, 14 and 20	5	8 and 14
3	50, 15 and 20	6	15 and 9

PAGE 23
Dividing
1	4	5	8
2	8	6	6
3	7	7	9
4	9	8	14g

Missing number problems
1	7	5	6
2	8	6	14
3	5	7	5
4	9	8	6

PAGE 25
Adding 2-digit numbers
1   37 → c
    75 → a
    58 → t
2   63 → d
    81 → o
    49 → g
3   49 → g
    81 → o
    75 → a
    58 → t
4   58 → t
    81 → o
    75 → a
    63 → d

Counting on
1	23	4	21
2	45	5	23
3	32	6	57

PAGE 27
Written method for adding
1	665	3	700
2	790	4	423
5	901	7	802
6	642	8	903

Adding money
1	£4.99	5	£2.34
2	£2.18	6	£1.76
3	£4.15	7	£4.49
4	£1.97	8	£2.72

PAGE 29
Column method
1	338	6	456
2	20	7	239
3	388	8	244
4	608	9	339
5	203		

Number line method
1	45	3	185
2	20	4	173

PAGE 31
Mental calculations
×	14	19	17
5	70	95	85
3	42	57	51

Written methods
1   112
2   324
3

120	27

120 + 27 = 147

4

350	15

350 + 15 = 365

5	74	8	220
6	285	9	252
7	172	10	171

PAGE 33
Doubling and halving
1	18	5	43
2	32	6	13
3	74	7	29
4	90	8	24

Division and remainders
1	22r2	5	47
2	19r3	6	4
3	22r3	7	4
4	17r1		

PAGE 35
Fractions of shapes
1	$\frac{1}{2}$	4	$\frac{1}{4}$
2	$\frac{1}{3}$	5	$\frac{1}{4}$
3	$\frac{1}{5}$	6	$\frac{1}{2}$

Fractions and division

1 4	6 12
2 4	7 4
3 7	8 8
4 2	9 3
5 6	

PAGE 37
Lines of symmetry

1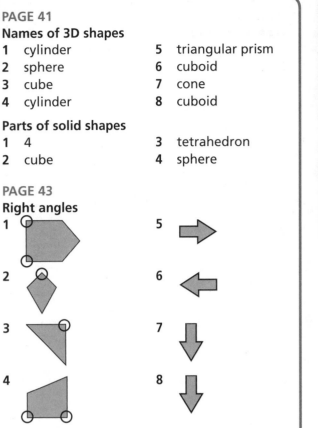

2

3

4 Any one of these lines of symmetry

5

6 Either of these lines of symmetry

7

8 Any one of these lines of symmetry

Reflections

1

2

3

4

PAGE 39
Polygons

1 6 sides – hexagon
2 6 sides – hexagon
3 3 sides – triangle
4 5 sides – pentagon
5 8 sides – octagon
6 7 sides – heptagon

Regular polygons

Shape	Property of shape		
	4 sides	A regular shape	1 or more right angles
	✔	✗	✔
	✗	✔	✗
	✗	✗	✔
	✔	✔	✔
	✗	✔	✗

PAGE 41
Names of 3D shapes

1 cylinder
2 sphere
3 cube
4 cylinder
5 triangular prism
6 cuboid
7 cone
8 cuboid

Parts of solid shapes

1 4
2 cube
3 tetrahedron
4 sphere

PAGE 43
Right angles

1

2

3

4

5

6

7

8

Types of angles

1 c
2 b
3 a
4 e
5 a
6 c and d
7 b
8 b

PAGE 45
Coordinates

1 (1,2)   2 (2,4)   3 (4,8)

4

Points of the compass
1 & 2

Directions
1 South
2 West
3 South-East

PAGE 47

Units of measure

1	14cm	4	60g
2	2 litre	5	3km
3	2m		

Converting units

1	4000ml	4	3500g
2	5500m	5	120mm
3	700cm		

Reading scales

1	2cm	2	25mm

PAGE 49

Finding perimeters

1	124m	3	11cm
2	5m	4	7cm

Finding areas

1	4 square cm	3	9 square cm
2	7 square cm	4	6 square cm

PAGE 51

Time facts

1	28 days	4	36 months
2	90 minutes	5	1 day
3	Monday	6	30th April

Telling the time

PAGE 53

Bar charts

1 90 km/h

2 Hare

3

4 Antelope

Pictograms

1	Tuesday	4	11
2	4	5	3
3	Thursday		

PAGE 55

Venn diagrams

Carroll diagrams

	1 or more right angles	No right angles
Quadrilateral	c, d	f, h
Not a quadrilateral	b, e	a, g

Letts Educational
4 Grosvenor Place, London SW1X 7DL
Orders: 015395 64910
Enquiries: 015395 65921
Email: enquiries@lettsandlonsdale.co.uk
Website: www.lettsandlonsdale.com

First published 2009

Editorial and design: 2ibooks [publishing solutions] Cambridge

Author: Paul Broadbent
Book concept and development: Helen Jacobs, Publishing Director
Editorial: Sophie London, Senior Commissioning Editor
Katy Knight, Junior Editor
Illustrators: Andy Roberts and Phillip Burrows
Cover design: Angela English

British Library Cataloging in Publication Data. A CIP record of this book is available from the British Library.

ISBN 9781844192175

Text, design and illustration © 2008 Letts Educational Ltd

Printed in Malta

Letts Educational make every effort to ensure that all paper used in our books is made from wood pulp obtained from well-managed forests, controlled sources and recycled wood or fibre.

Mental calculations

Write the missing numbers to complete this multiplication grid.

×	14	19	17
5			
3			

14 x 3

Written methods

Answer these.

1 $28 \times 4 =$

$$\begin{array}{r} 28 \\ \times\ 4 \\ \hline \end{array}$$

2 $54 \times 6 =$

$$\begin{array}{r} 54 \\ \times\ 6 \\ \hline \end{array}$$

3 $49 \times 3 =$

×	40	9
3		

☐ + ☐ = ☐

4 $73 \times 5 =$

×	70	3
5		

☐ + ☐ = ☐

5 What is thirty-seven multiplied by two? ☐

6 Calculate 95×3. ☐

7 A shop has 86 pairs of shoes. How many shoes are there altogether? ☐

8 Golf balls are sold in packs of five. How many balls will there be in 44 packs? ☐

9 A baker has baked enough rolls to fill 63 bags with 4 rolls each. How many bread rolls did he bake in total? ☐

10 A school uses three 57-seater buses for a trip to a museum. All the seats are filled. How many tickets will be needed for the museum? ☐

TOTAL MARKS ☐ 16

Division

Doubling and halving

An important thing to remember about division is that it is the inverse or opposite of multiplication.

$40 \div 2 = $ _____ $20 \times 2 = 40$

It is very useful to be able to double and halve numbers. Look at this doubling machine.

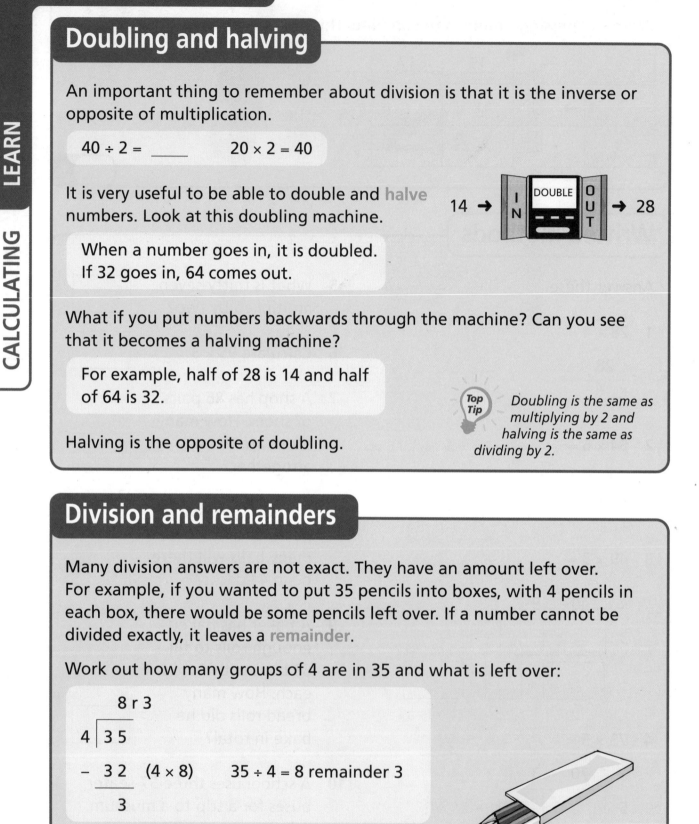

14 → IN DOUBLE OUT → 28

When a number goes in, it is doubled. If 32 goes in, 64 comes out.

What if you put numbers backwards through the machine? Can you see that it becomes a halving machine?

For example, half of 28 is 14 and half of 64 is 32.

Halving is the opposite of doubling.

Top Tip *Doubling is the same as multiplying by 2 and halving is the same as dividing by 2.*

Division and remainders

Many division answers are not exact. They have an amount left over. For example, if you wanted to put 35 pencils into boxes, with 4 pencils in each box, there would be some pencils left over. If a number cannot be divided exactly, it leaves a remainder.

Work out how many groups of 4 are in 35 and what is left over:

```
      8 r 3
   ┌───────
 4 │ 3 5
   - 3 2   (4 × 8)
   ───────
      3
```

$35 \div 4 = 8$ remainder 3

🔑 **Key words**   halve   remainder

Doubling and halving

Write the missing numbers for each function machine.

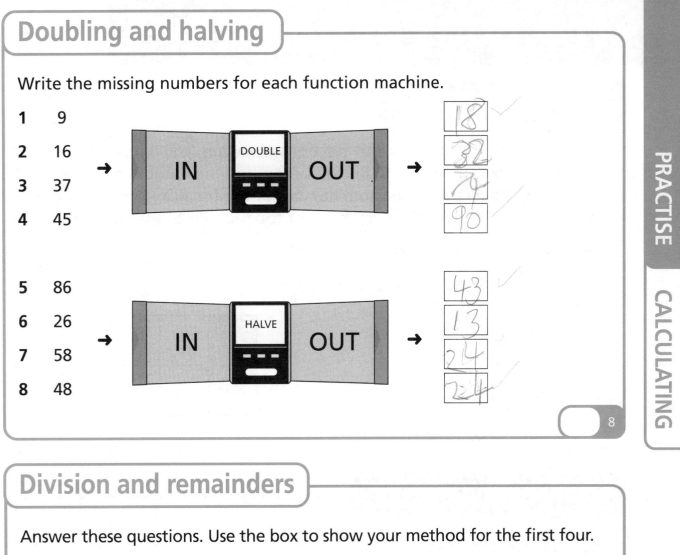

1 9
2 16
3 37
4 45

IN → DOUBLE → OUT

18 ✓
32
74
90

5 86
6 26
7 58
8 48

IN → HALVE → OUT

43 ✓
13
24
24

8

Division and remainders

Answer these questions. Use the box to show your method for the first four.

1 $3\overline{)68}$ = 26 r 2

2 $79 \div 4$ = 12 r 31

3 $4\overline{)91}$ = 20 r 11

4 $52 \div 3$ = 10 r 52

Method box:
$4\overline{)79}$
$3\overline{)52}$
$6\overline{)52}$

5 Circle the number that has a remainder of 2 when divided by 5.

33   68   (47)   54

6 What is the remainder when you divide fifty-two by six?   4

7 Twenty-five eggs are put into boxes holding six eggs each.
There is one egg left over.
How many egg boxes are used?   4

7

TOTAL MARKS 15

Fractions of quantities

Fractions of shapes

When you are asked to work out fractions of shapes, you may need to work out equivalent fractions. Remember to find the number of equal parts (the denominator or bottom number of the fraction) and then how many parts are shaded (the numerator or top number of the fraction).

What fraction of the rectangle is shaded?

The rectangle is divided into 8 equal parts and 2 parts are shaded.

$$\frac{2}{8} \begin{array}{c} \div 2 \\ \div 2 \end{array} = \frac{1}{4}$$

Fractions and division

Look at these examples.

What is:

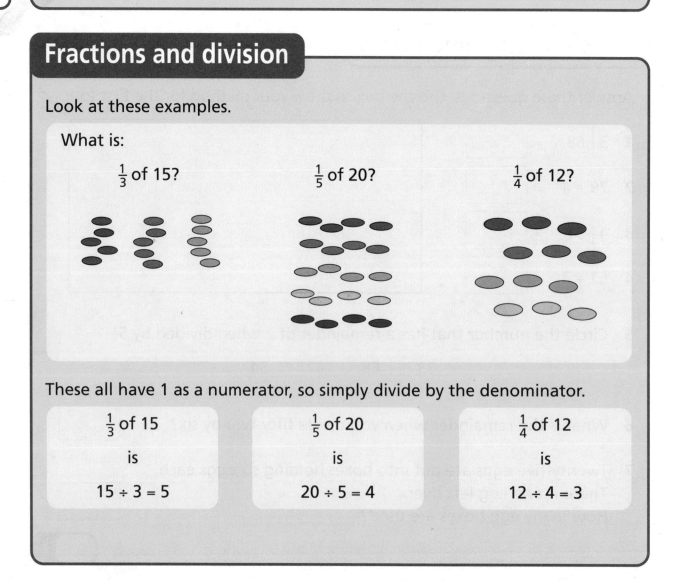

$\frac{1}{3}$ of 15?	$\frac{1}{5}$ of 20?	$\frac{1}{4}$ of 12?

These all have 1 as a numerator, so simply divide by the denominator.

$\frac{1}{3}$ of 15	$\frac{1}{5}$ of 20	$\frac{1}{4}$ of 12
is	is	is
$15 \div 3 = 5$	$20 \div 5 = 4$	$12 \div 4 = 3$

Fractions of shapes

What fraction of each shape is shaded red?

1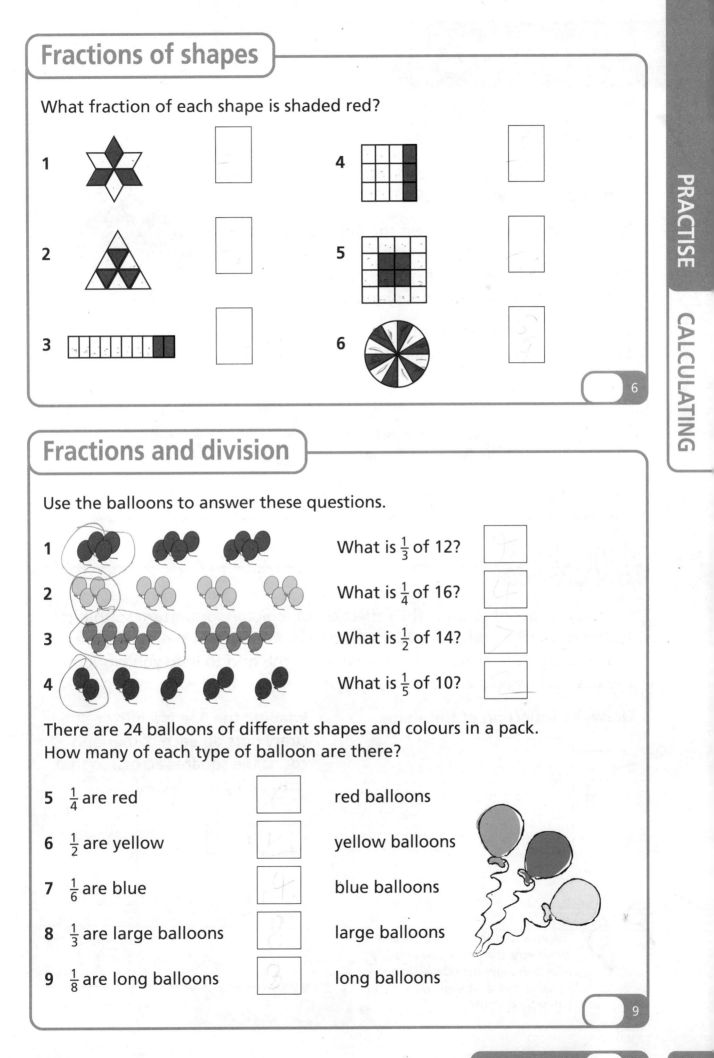

2

3

4

5

6

6

Fractions and division

Use the balloons to answer these questions.

1   What is $\frac{1}{3}$ of 12?

2   What is $\frac{1}{4}$ of 16?

3   What is $\frac{1}{2}$ of 14?

4   What is $\frac{1}{5}$ of 10?

There are 24 balloons of different shapes and colours in a pack.
How many of each type of balloon are there?

5   $\frac{1}{4}$ are red   red balloons

6   $\frac{1}{2}$ are yellow   yellow balloons

7   $\frac{1}{6}$ are blue   blue balloons

8   $\frac{1}{3}$ are large balloons   large balloons

9   $\frac{1}{8}$ are long balloons   long balloons

9

Symmetry

Lines of symmetry

Some shapes are **symmetrical** – they have lines of symmetry. Look at the shape.

If you imagine it folded down the middle, the two sides would look exactly the same. That fold line is the line of symmetry and shows if a shape or pattern is symmetrical.

These letters are symmetrical.
Can you see the lines of symmetry?

A - B - C - D

Reflections

You may be asked to draw the reflection of a picture or pattern so that it is symmetrical. The mirror line is always drawn to help and the shapes are usually drawn on a grid. Use the squares on the grid to help you work out the position of each corner of the shape.

Draw the reflection of this shape.

Imagine the line is a mirror. Draw dots on each corner and count the squares across, so that each point is reflected.

Top Tip *When a mirror is put on the line of symmetry, the half shape and its reflection show the whole shape. Practise using a small mirror to help you find symmetrical shapes.*

Key words | **symmetrical**

Lines of symmetry

Draw one line of symmetry on each of these shapes.

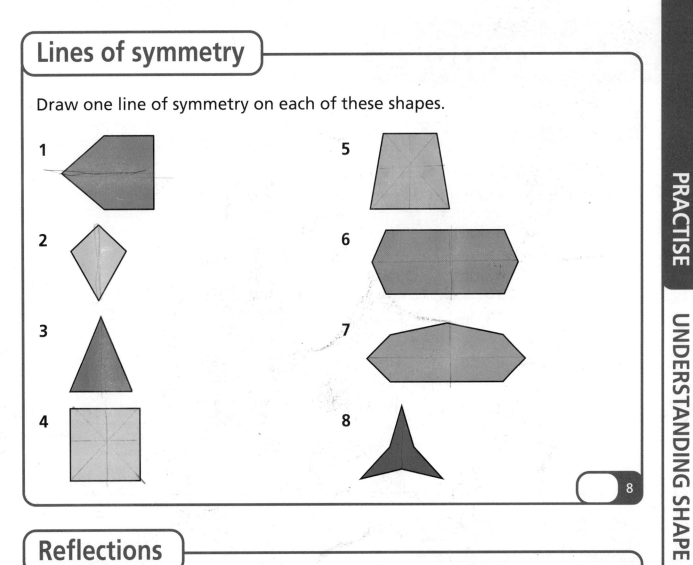

1

2

3

4

5

6

7

8

8

Reflections

Complete these reflections.

1 Use a ruler to draw lines to make a symmetrical shape about the mirror line.

2 Shade in the reflection of this shape. You may use a mirror.

3 Here is a square with a design on it. The square is reflected in the mirror line. Draw the missing stripe and circle on the reflected square.

4 Draw the reflection of this triangle.

4

TOTAL MARKS 12

2D shapes

Polygons

Any shape with straight sides is called a **polygon**.
The name of the polygon tells you the number of sides.

3 sides	Triangle	
4 sides	Quadrilateral	
5 sides	Pentagon	
6 sides	Hexagon	
7 sides	Heptagon	
8 sides	Octagon	

Regular polygons

Regular polygons are shapes with all sides of equal length and all angles the same size.

Some regular shapes have special names.

A regular triangle is an **equilateral triangle**.

A regular quadrilateral is a **square**.

Another special four-sided shape is a **rectangle**.
It has four **right angles** and two pairs of
parallel sides, which are the same length.

Top Tip *When you look at shapes, check their sides and angles. Remember that parallel sides never meet and right angles are like square angles.*

Key words   polygon   right angle   parallel

Polygons

Count the number of sides and write the name of each shape.

1 ☐ _____

2 ☐ _____

3 ☐ _____

4 ☐ _____

5 ☐ _____

6 ☐ _____

6

Regular polygons

Complete this table. Write in the missing cross (✗) or tick (✔) in each space.

Shape	Property of shape		
	4 sides	A regular shape	1 or more right angles
		✗	
	✗		
			✔
	✔		
			✗

10

TOTAL MARKS ☐ 16

3D solids

Names of 3D shapes

Solid shapes are 3-dimensional. You need to learn the names and properties of these 3D shapes.

cube   cuboid   cylinder   tetrahedron

cone   triangular prism   sphere   square-based pyramid

Top Tip
A cube is a special cuboid and a cuboid is a type of prism. Can you see how a cuboid has some properties similar to a triangular prism?

Parts of solid shapes

Solid shapes are made up of **faces**, **edges** and **vertices** or corners.

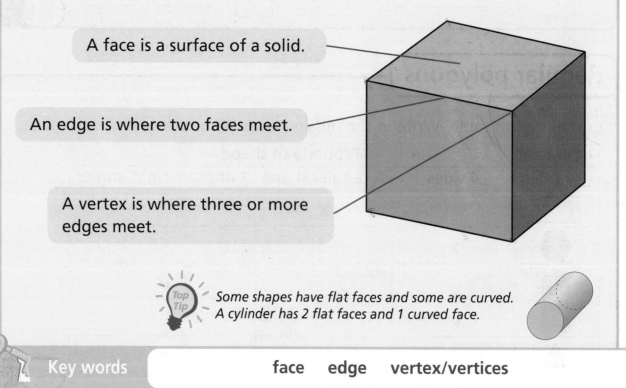

A face is a surface of a solid.

An edge is where two faces meet.

A vertex is where three or more edges meet.

Top Tip
Some shapes have flat faces and some are curved. A cylinder has 2 flat faces and 1 curved face.

Key words   face   edge   vertex/vertices

Names of 3D shapes

Write the shape name of each of these everyday objects.

1 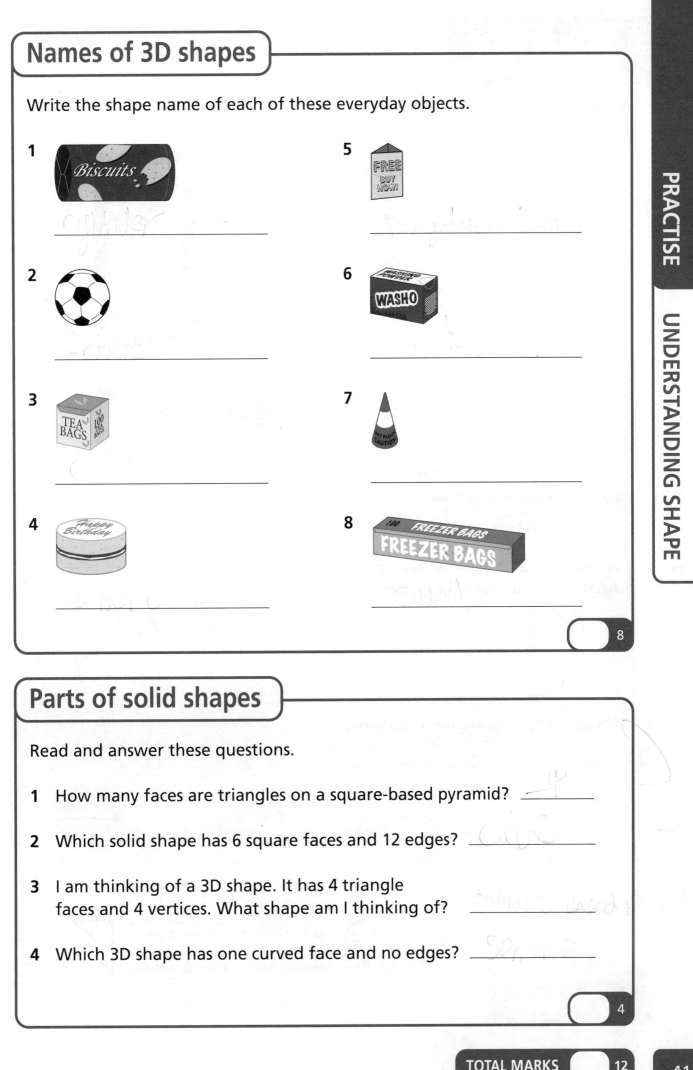 cylinder

5 _____

2 _____

6 _____

3 _____

7 _____

4 _____

8 Cuboid

8

Parts of solid shapes

Read and answer these questions.

1 How many faces are triangles on a square-based pyramid? ___4___

2 Which solid shape has 6 square faces and 12 edges? ___cube___

3 I am thinking of a 3D shape. It has 4 triangle faces and 4 vertices. What shape am I thinking of? _____

4 Which 3D shape has one curved face and no edges? _____

4

TOTAL MARKS   12

Angles

Right angles

Corners of doors, windows, books and tables all show right angles.

These are **square angles** and can be seen all around us.

A right angle is a quarter turn, **clockwise** or **anticlockwise**.

Squares and rectangles have four right angles – one at each corner.

Types of angles

An angle is a measure of turn between two lines.
Angles are measured in degrees (°).

There are 360° in a full circle.

90°	90°
90°	90°

These are special angles to remember.

| 180° (straight line) | 90° (right angle) | **acute** angle (less than a right angle) | **obtuse** angle (between 90° and 180°) |

Top Tip

Use a right-angle corner from a piece of paper to compare angles, to see if they are acute or obtuse.

Key words   **clockwise   anticlockwise   acute   obtuse**

Right angles

Circle all of the right angles on each shape.

1   **2**   **3**   **4**

Read the instructions and circle the arrow pointing in the correct direction.

5   This arrow is rotated 90° clockwise.

6   This arrow is rotated 90° anticlockwise.

7   This arrow is rotated 90° anticlockwise.

8   This arrow is rotated 90° clockwise.

8

Types of angles

Look at these angles and answer the questions.

a   b   c   d   e

1   Which is the smallest angle?

2   Which angle is a straight line?

3   Which is a right angle?

4   Which angle is obtuse?

5   Which angle is 90°?

6   Which two angles are acute?

     and

7   Which angle is 180°?

8   Which is the largest angle?

8

TOTAL MARKS   16

Position and direction

Coordinates

Coordinates are used to show the exact position of a point on a grid.

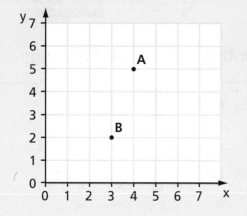

The coordinates of **A** are (4,5).

The coordinates of **B** are (3,2).

Coordinates are always written in brackets and separated by a comma.

Remember to read the horizontal number along the bottom and then the vertical number up the side.

Points of the compass

It is useful to know the points of the compass. North and South are opposite each other, as are East and West. In between these are the other four points. Look at the way their names always start with North or South.

Top Tip
To remember the order of the four main directions, look at the initials NESW. A well-known saying to learn this order is Naughty Elephants Squirt Water!

Directions

Clockwise and anticlockwise are instructions for moving in different directions. Quarter turns, half turns and whole turns are used to describe how far to turn.

This arrow has moved a quarter turn clockwise.

This arrow has moved a half turn anticlockwise.

A whole turn is a complete circle. This is a whole turn clockwise.

Key words | horizontal   vertical

Coordinates

1   Circle the correct coordinates for point **A**.

   (1,1)   (1,2)   (2,1)   (2,2)

2   Write the coordinates for point **B**.

   (⬜ , ⬜)

3   Write the coordinates for point **C**.

   (8 , 8)

4   Draw a cross at (5,10) and label it **D**.

4

Points of the compass

The arrow labelled N is pointing North.

1   Label the arrows pointing South, West and East.

2   Colour the arrow pointing North-West.

2

Directions

Look at the compass points to help you answer these.

1   If I face North and make a half turn clockwise, which direction will I be facing?   _____

2   If I face South and make a quarter turn clockwise, which direction will I be facing?   East

3   If I face North-West and make a half turn anticlockwise, which direction will I be facing?   West

3

TOTAL MARKS   9

Measures

Units of measure

Length, weight (or mass) and capacity are all measured using different units. Try to learn these:

Length	1 centimetre (cm) = 10 millimetres (mm) 1 metre (m) = 100 centimetres (cm) 1 kilometre (km) = 1000 metres (m)
Weight	1 kilogram (kg) = 1000 grams (g)
Capacity	1 litre (l) = 1000 millilitres (ml)

Top Tip *Remember to always write the units in your answers. There is a big difference between 100g and 100kg!*

Converting units

Once you know these **equivalent** measures, then you can convert from one unit to another. This always means multiplying or dividing by 10, 100 or 1000, depending on what you are converting.

My finger is 6.3cm or 63mm long.

A lemonade bottle holds 3000ml or 3 litres.

This cake weighs 1.3kg or 1300g.

20 times around a 400m running track is 8000m or 8km.

Reading scales

A scale is the marking of lines to help us measure, e.g. up the side of a jug, on weighing scales or on a ruler. You need to read them carefully, using these steps:

1 Look at the unit – is it ml, cm, mm, g ... ?

2 If the line is level with a number, read off that number.

3 If the line is between numbers, work out what each mark means and count on or back.

Key words equivalent

Units of measure

Underline the amount each item is most likely to measure.

1 My pencil is (14mm) (14cm) (14m) (14km) long.

2 I bought a (2ml) (20ml) (2 litre) (20 litre) carton of milk.

3 The classroom door is (2mm) (2cm) (2m) (2km) high.

4 An apple weighs (6g) (60g) (6kg) (60kg).

5 I travel (3mm) (3cm) (3m) (3km) to school every day.

5

Converting units

Answer these questions.

1 How many millilitres are there in four litres? `4000` ml

2 How many metres are there in five and a half kilometres? `5500` m

3 How many centimetres are there in seven metres? `700` cm

4 How many grams are there in three and a half kilograms? `3500` g

5 How many millimetres are there in twelve centimetres? `120` mm

5

Reading scales

Measure these sides with a ruler.

1 Use a ruler to measure the length of side **A**.
Give your answer in centimetres. `5` cm

2 Measure accurately the length of side **B**.
Give your answer in millimetres. `7000` mm

2

TOTAL MARKS 12

Perimeter and area

Finding perimeters

The **perimeter** of a shape is simply the distance all the way around the edge. These two shapes have the same perimeter of 16cm.

If the shape has straight sides, add up the lengths of all the sides. These may be given, or you may need to measure carefully along each of the sides using a ruler.

3cm + 3cm + 4cm + 4cm + 6cm = 20cm

The perimeter of this shape is 20cm.

If the shape has curved sides, a piece of string or cotton may be useful. Go around the edge of the shape and then measure the length of the piece of thread.

This shape has a perimeter of 10cm.

Finding areas

The **area** of a shape is the amount of surface that it covers. You can often measure the area of shapes by counting squares.

These shapes both have an area of 8 squares.

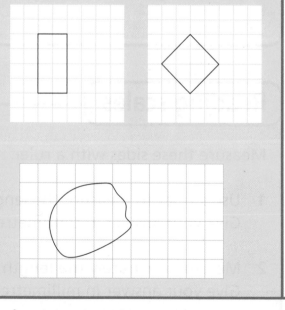

If the shape is not made up from whole squares, count all the squares that are bigger than a half.

This shape has an area of approximately 12 squares.

🔑 **Key words**   perimeter   area

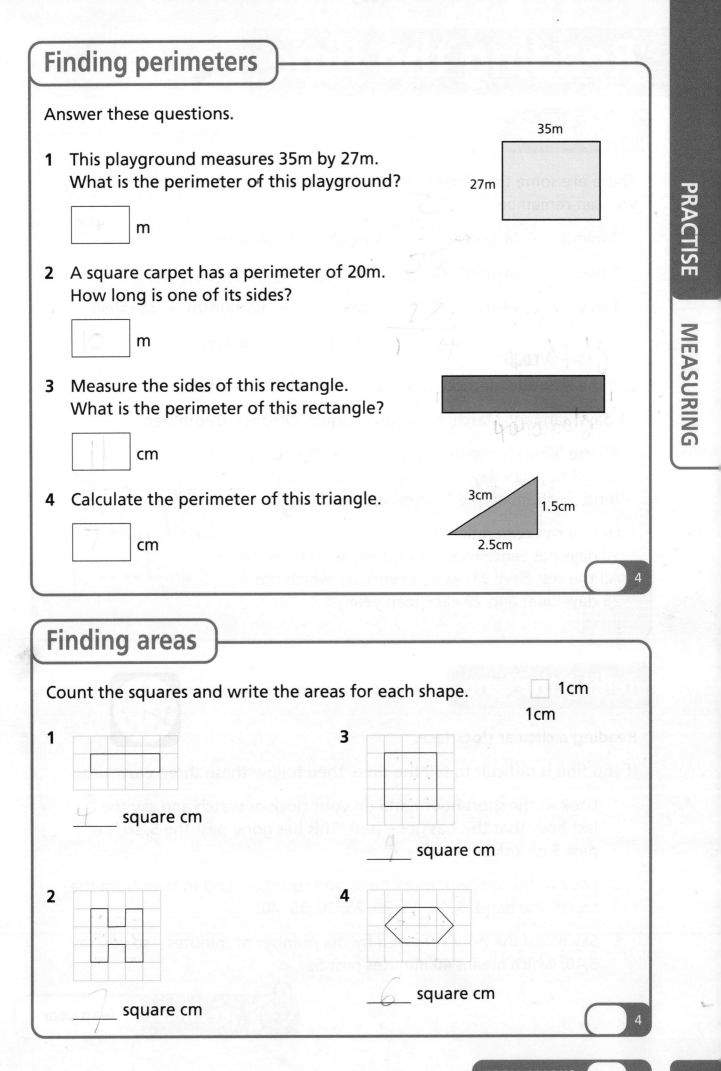

Finding perimeters

Answer these questions.

1 This playground measures 35m by 27m.
What is the perimeter of this playground?

[ ] **m**

35m

27m

2 A square carpet has a perimeter of 20m.
How long is one of its sides?

[10] **m**

3 Measure the sides of this rectangle.
What is the perimeter of this rectangle?

[11] **cm**

4 Calculate the perimeter of this triangle.

[7] **cm**

3cm
1.5cm
2.5cm

4

Finding areas

Count the squares and write the areas for each shape.

[ ] 1cm
1cm

1

___4___ square cm

3

___9___ square cm

2

___7___ square cm

4

___6___ square cm

4

TOTAL MARKS [ ] 8

Reading the time

Time facts

These are some time facts to learn. Cover each one up and see how many you can remember.

1 minute	= 60 seconds	1 week	= 7 days
1 hour	= 60 minutes	1 fortnight	= 14 days
1 day	= 24 hours	1 year	= 12 months = 365 days
		leap year	= 366 days

Use the 'knuckle method' to learn the days of the months:

31 days: January, March, May, July, August, October, December.

All the 'knuckle months' have 31 days. February has 28 days (29 days in a **leap year**) and April, June, September and November have 30 days.

Or you can remember:
30 days has September, April, June and November.
All the rest have 31, except February which has 28 days clear and 29 each leap year.

Telling the time

Reading a circular clock face.

If you find it difficult to tell the time, then follow these three easy steps.

1 Look at the short hour hand on your clock or watch and say the last hour that this has gone past. This has gone past the 5, so it is past 5 o'clock.

2 Look at the longer minute hand and count around in fives from the top to the hand: 5, 10, 15, 20, 25, 30, 35, 40.

3 Say aloud the hour followed by the number of minutes – so you say 5.40, which means 40 minutes past 5.

Key words   leap year

Time facts

Answer these questions.

1 How many days are there in four weeks? _____

2 A film is an hour and a half long.
   How many minutes is this? _____

3 If today is Monday 10th August, what day
   of the week will 17th August be? _____

4 How many months are there in three years? _____

5 How many more days are there in a leap year
   than a normal year? _____

6 If today is 1st May, what was the date yesterday? _____

6

Telling the time

Draw the missing hands to show these times. Remember to draw the hour hand shorter than the minute hand.

1 quarter past ten

2 6.10

3 twenty past eight

4 11.25

5 quarter to one

6 9.55

6

TOTAL MARKS 12

Handling data

Bar charts

Bar charts are a useful way of showing information. To understand bar charts and other types of graph, look carefully at the different parts of the graph.

1   Read the title – what is it all about? Is there any other information given?

2   Look at the axis labels – these should explain the lines that go up and across.

3   Work out the scale – look carefully at the numbers. Do they go up in 1s, 2s, 5s, 10s … ?

4   Compare the bars – read them across to work out the amounts.

Top Tip
The scale is very important. This graph goes up in tens and some of the bars are between tens. For example, there were between 40 and 50 visitors on Tuesday. To read this, go across from the top of the bar and count on from 40 to 42.

Pictograms

Pictograms use symbols or pictures, where each symbol represents a certain number of items.

This is a record of the numbers of frogs seen crossing a road in a morning.

Time	Number of frogs
7:00 – 8:00	🐸 🐸 🐸 🐸
8:00 – 9:00	🐸 🐸 🐸 🐸 🐸 🐸
9:00 – 10:00	🐸 🐸 🐸 🐸 🐸 🐸 🐸 🐸 🐸 🐸
10:00 – 11:00	🐸 🐸 🐸 🐸 🐸 🐸
11:00 – 12:00	🐸 🐸 🐸

🐸 = 2 frogs

Top Tip
Check what each individual picture stands for. This shows that 12 frogs were seen between 8.00 and 9.00am.

Key words   axis

Bar charts

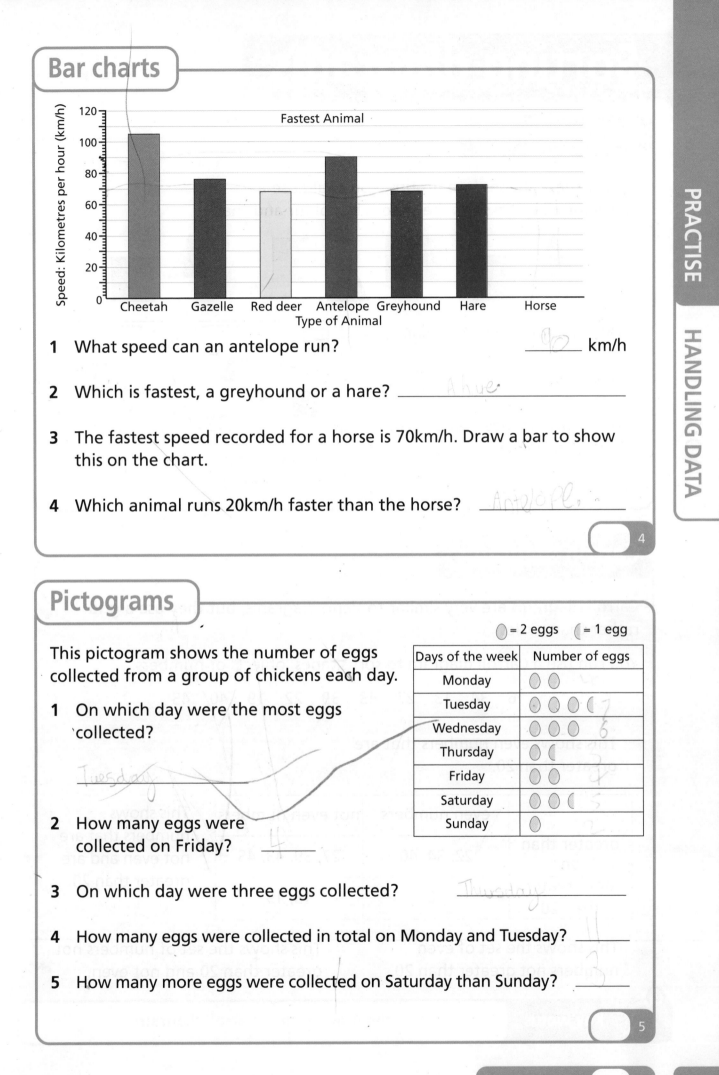

Fastest Animal

Speed: Kilometres per hour (km/h)

Type of Animal

Cheetah Gazelle Red deer Antelope Greyhound Hare Horse

1 What speed can an antelope run? _____ 90 km/h

2 Which is fastest, a greyhound or a hare? _____ Hare

3 The fastest speed recorded for a horse is 70km/h. Draw a bar to show this on the chart.

4 Which animal runs 20km/h faster than the horse? _____ Antelope.

4

Pictograms

○ = 2 eggs   (= 1 egg

This pictogram shows the number of eggs collected from a group of chickens each day.

Days of the week	Number of eggs
Monday	○ ○
Tuesday	○ ○ ○ (
Wednesday	○ ○ ○
Thursday	○ (
Friday	○ ○
Saturday	○ ○ (
Sunday	○

1 On which day were the most eggs collected?

_____ Tuesday

2 How many eggs were collected on Friday? _____ 4

3 On which day were three eggs collected? _____ Thursday

4 How many eggs were collected in total on Monday and Tuesday? _____ 4

5 How many more eggs were collected on Saturday than Sunday? _____ 3

5

Sorting diagrams

HANDLING DATA   LEARN

Venn diagrams

To sort these shapes into groups, you could use a Venn diagram.
This Venn diagram sorts the shapes by colour and shape.

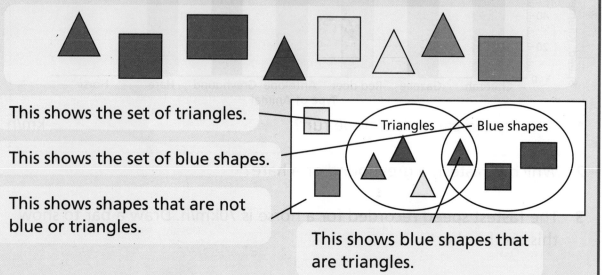

This shows the set of triangles.

This shows the set of blue shapes.

This shows shapes that are not blue or triangles.

This shows blue shapes that are triangles.

Carroll diagrams

Carroll diagrams are very similar to Venn diagrams, but they use a grid rather than circles.

You can use a Carroll diagram to sort shapes, objects or numbers.

16   34   13   27   43   39   22   19   40   45

This shows even numbers that are greater than 20.

	even numbers	not even numbers
greater than 20	22, 34, 40	27, 39, 43, 45
not greater than 20	16	13, 19

This shows numbers that are not even and are greater than 20.

This shows the set of even numbers not greater than 20.

This shows the set of numbers not greater than 20 and not even.

Key words   Venn diagram   Carroll diagram

Venn diagrams

Write the letter for each creature in the correct section of this Venn diagram. Then you could have a go at drawing them too!

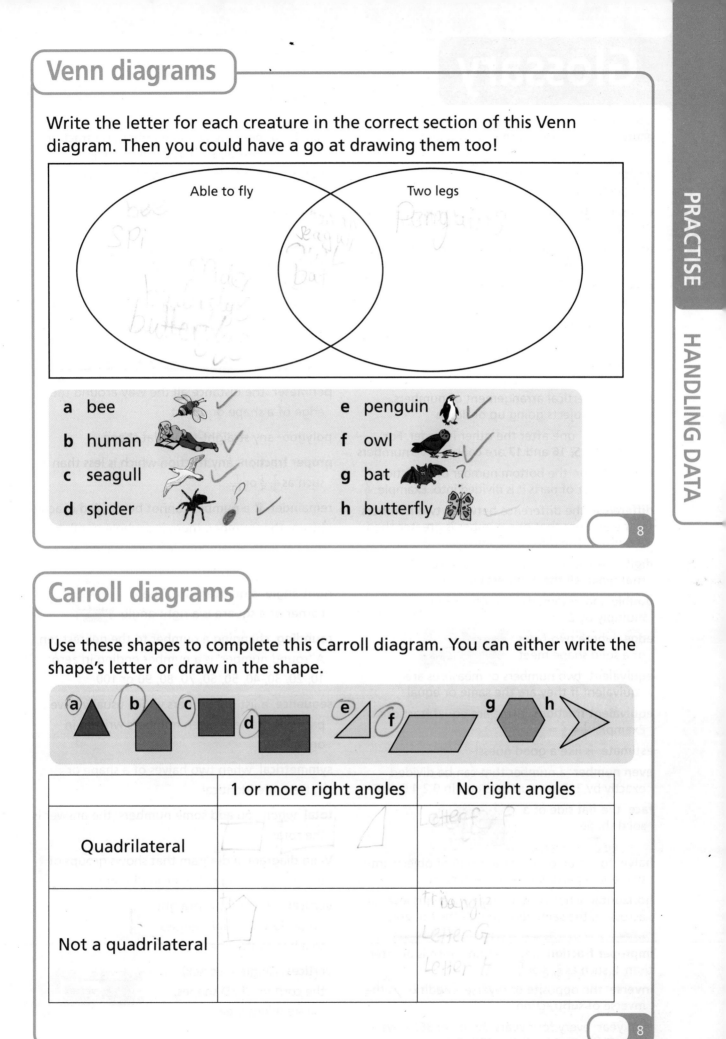

Able to fly   Two legs

a bee	**e** penguin
b human	**f** owl
c seagull	**g** bat
d spider	**h** butterfly

8

Carroll diagrams

Use these shapes to complete this Carroll diagram. You can either write the shape's letter or draw in the shape.

a   b   c   d   e   f   g   h

	1 or more right angles	No right angles
Quadrilateral		Letter f
Not a quadrilateral		triangle Letter G Letter h

8

TOTAL MARKS   16

Glossary

acute an angle smaller than a right angle

anticlockwise turning in this direction

approximate answer a 'rough' answer – near to the real answer

area the area of a shape is the amount of surface that it covers

axis (plural is axes) the horizontal and vertical lines on a graph

Carroll diagram a grid used to sort things into groups or sets

clockwise turning in this direction

column a vertical arrangement of numbers, words or objects going up or down

consecutive one after the other in order. For example, 15, 16 and 17 are consecutive numbers

denominator the bottom number of a fraction, the number of parts it is divided into. Example: $\frac{2}{3}$

difference the difference between two numbers is the amount that one number is greater than the other. The difference between 18 and 21 is 3

digit there are 10 digits: 0 1 2 3 4 5 6 7 8 and 9 that make all the numbers we use

double make something twice as big, or multiply by 2

edge where two faces of a solid shape meet

equivalent two numbers or measures are equivalent if they are the same or equal

equivalent fractions these are equal fractions. Example: $\frac{1}{2} = \frac{2}{4} = \frac{3}{6}$

estimate is like a good guess

even number a number that can be divided exactly by 2. Even numbers end in 0 2 4 6 or 8

face the flat side of a solid shape

halve to cut an object or a group of objects into two equal parts, so there is $\frac{1}{2}$ in each

horizontal a horizontal line is a straight level line across, in the same direction as the horizon

improper fraction any fraction which is greater than 1, such as $\frac{5}{3}$, $\frac{8}{5}$ or $\frac{6}{2}$

inverse the opposite or reverse – addition is the inverse of subtraction

leap year every four years there are 366 days in a year. The extra day is the 29th February

mixed number any whole number and fraction written together, such as $2\frac{1}{2}$, $4\frac{3}{5}$ or $1\frac{3}{10}$

multiple a multiple is a number made by multiplying together two other numbers

numerator the top number of a fraction. Example: $\frac{3}{5}$

obtuse an angle less than 180° (a straight line) but greater than 90° (a right angle)

parallel lines that are parallel never meet and the distance between the lines remains the same

perimeter the distance all the way around the edge of a shape or object

polygon any straight-sided flat shape

proper fraction any fraction which is less than 1, such as $\frac{2}{3}$, $\frac{3}{5}$ or $\frac{1}{10}$

remainder if a number cannot be divided exactly by another number, there is a whole number answer with an amount left over, called a remainder

right angle a quarter turn. The corner of a square is a right angle

rounding changing a number to the nearest ten. A 'round number' is a number ending in zero: 10, 20, 30, 40, 50, 60, 70, 80, 90 or 100

sequence a list of numbers which usually have a pattern. They are often numbers written in order

symmetrical when two halves of a shape or pattern are identical

total when you add some numbers, the answer is the total

Venn diagram a diagram that shows groups of things by putting circles around them

vertical a line that is straight up or down, at right angles to a horizontal line

vertices (single is vertex) the corners of 3D shapes, where edges meet

Notes

NOTES

57

Notes